The Conquest of Morpeth

Bridget Gubbins

Stories of battles, romance and wickedness

Bridget Gubbins
Illustrations by Susan Dibben

By the same author

Juliana and Ranulph of Morpeth Castle, 2016
Newminster, Monks, Shepherds and Charters, 2014
The Mysteries of Morpeth's Workhouse, 2013
The Drovers are Coming to Morpeth Town, 2012
The Curious Yards and Alleyways of Morpeth, 2011

Published by
Greater Morpeth Development Trust
Carlisle Park Lodge
Castle Square
Morpeth
Northumberland
NE61 1YD

**Greater Morpeth
Development Trust**
Regeneration of town & countryside

British Library Cataloguing in Publication Data
A catalogue reference for this book is available from the British Library

ISBN 978-0-9568683-7-4

Cover design by Azure Printing

Printed in Great Britain by Azure Printing, Unit 1 F & G, Pegswood Industrial Estate, Pegswood, Morpeth, Northumberland NE61 6HZ

Dear young readers

The stories in this book really happened. They are not like fairy stories which have happy endings.

The children in them had few choices about their lives. Unlike you, they couldn't decide what they would be when they grew up.

If their father was a nobleman, the boys were expected to be warriors and the girls to marry and produce sons.

Children from poor families had even less choice. Like their mothers and fathers, they would be poor all their lives.

Except for the two child servants whose names and lives I have invented, all the people in these stories really lived in Northumberland and Morpeth. I have found their adventures in ancient books and documents. There is no record of the words they actually spoke, so I have imagined those myself.

They are your very own history, and I have been glad to write them for you. Perhaps you too might like to write stories about boys and girls from times long ago. I hope so.

Yours sincerely

Bridget Gubbins
Morpeth, 2017

1066

William de Merlay's story

1072

Edmund's story

1080 - 1095

Robert de Mowbray's story

1095

Matilda's story

1113

Juliana's story

1120

Ebba's story

1129

Eustorcia's story

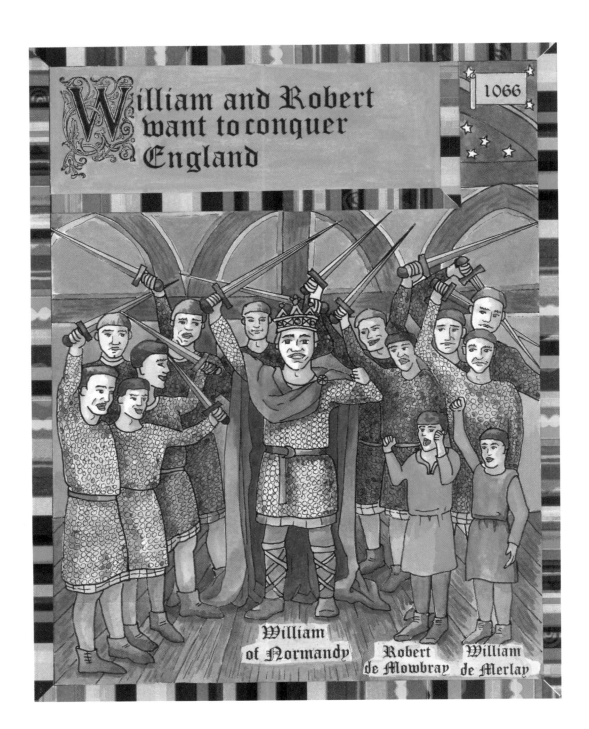

William de Merlay – the boy from Normandy 1066

My name is William de Merlay. I come from a little place called Le Merlerault in Normandy, far away across the sea. Although I am only a boy, I am helping to conquer England, and I want to earn power and riches for myself. I would like to have my own castle and rule over the English people. I am a Norman.

In the hall of Normandy

Not long ago, I was in a great hall with my friend Robert. All the noblemen of Normandy were there. Our leader was the brave Duke William. He said that he, not King Harold, was the rightful king of England.

Duke William called out to us: "Who is brave enough to follow me to conquer England?"

There was an enormous roar and swords were clashed on shields in the great hall. "We'll go with you," the noblemen all shouted, and so did Robert and I.

We really wanted this adventure. We would win lands for our duke, and perhaps we would gain castles for ourselves. At that time, we were about twelve years old. We were both servants of the great bishop Geoffrey of Coutances, and he was Robert's uncle. He had built a beautiful cathedral in Normandy, and was one of Duke William's most important men.

We boys were proud to be among his followers. We knew that if we followed him faithfully, and if we won the battles, we would be well rewarded.

"It is time for us to prepare the boats to go to England," Bishop Geoffrey said to us. "You are young, and are my best servants. Always obey my orders, and if God is willing, you will have great adventures and riches."

There were other bishops and many important noblemen and soldiers getting ready to go to England. We helped to prepare the boats and gather the warhorses and the food supplies. Then we loaded the horses on to the boats. At first, the wind was in the wrong direction, but at last we were able to sail, and we arrived on the south coast of England, a long way from Northumberland.

The battle of Hastings

We knew there would soon be a great battle. King Harold of England and our duke were enemies. We Normans were camped on a hill, and the English army was on another. Robert and I and the other servants had to make sure that the weapons for our lords were ready, the lances and helmets gleaming, and the armour for the horses in order. Everyone was excited, but fearful too.

"I am afraid," I whispered to Robert. "If we are killed in battle we might go to hell for evermore. The devils will burn us up in endless fires."

"They might cut out our tongues and roast us on spears," said Robert. We became really frightened. As we were sitting round the camp fires, looking at the English over the valley, our lord Bishop Geoffrey came to us.

"Confess your sins, my young men," he said to us. "God will save you from hell if you die with a clean soul. Let me bless you and ask God to forgive your sins."

So we made a promise to God. We would stop ourselves from eating meat one day every week if we escaped from the battle alive and well. We spent most of the night praying and singing psalms and confessing our sins. But the English – they were different. They were drinking and rioting and feasting all night long. There was noise and chaos as they tumbled over each other, fighting and falling down. That is what I remember.

The next day there was a terrible battle near a place called Hastings. Our soldiers killed King Harold of England and many of his men, and drove the others away. We were victorious.

The coronation of William the Conqueror

We marched to London where our duke was to be crowned the new king of England in the abbey of Westminster.

All the Normans and many English people were in the abbey ready for the coronation. Our language is French and we didn't understand English at that time. The archbishop is the person who crowns the king. Holding the crown over our duke's head, he called out to all the people in the church in English: "Do you accept this man as your king?"

The English people cried out: "Yes, we do!"

But the Norman people didn't understand the English words and they began to shout angrily.

Bishop Geoffrey knew what to do. Standing up in front of all the people, he spoke the same words in the French language: "Do you accept this man as your king?"

And the Normans who then understood shouted: "Oui, oui!" in French.

Unfortunately, the guards outside the abbey heard the shouts and thought a riot was starting. They panicked, and set fire to the houses near the abbey. When the men and women in the church saw the flames, they rushed outside. Some put out the flames, but others took their chance to commit robberies in the confusion.

Our duke was much alarmed while all this was going on, but with his hands trembling the archbishop placed the crown upon his head. In this way, Duke William of Normandy was crowned King William of England.

This is just the start of the conquest of England. Many people are still fighting the Normans, but our lord, Bishop Geoffrey, always helps King William. Now we are following him in his battles, always obeying his orders. We are growing into men, becoming stronger and braver all the time. Even though I am young, I have sometimes pierced an Englishman with my sword and lance, and even killed a few. One time I was wounded in my shoulder, but I did not die.

Why does a bishop fight and kill?
One thing puzzles me. Not long ago, I asked Bishop Geoffrey my question.

"My lord bishop, you are a man of God. Our church tells us not to kill. So why do you fight and kill your enemies?"

He replied: "These battles are righteous. God is on our side. King William is the rightful king of England. And you know that I do not kill our enemies with my own hands. That is not for a bishop to do, but for his soldiers."

It is true. Both Robert and I have wounded and even killed some Englishmen, and seen many of our own side killed too. But never has Bishop Geoffrey done that with his own hand. Despite his answer, I am still puzzled about it.

While I follow Bishop Geoffrey, I am waiting for my chance to be rewarded with a castle and great lands in England. I wonder where that will be?

My name is Edmund. I am a servant boy to one of the great lords of Northumbria called Gospatric. I shall tell you the story of how my lord fought the Normans who were conquering our land.

Battle against the invaders

I was hiding in a corner in the castle at Bamburgh listening to an argument between my lord Gospatric and his wife. She was begging him not to go to war.

"My husband, please don't go off to battle with this new King William. What will become of us if we lose? What will happen to the children and the old people? The king's men will drive us from our homes and we will suffer and die."

"Listen to me, my wife," shouted Gospatric. "Are we going to let these strangers take our land? Rule us and tax us and make us bow down before them?"

"But perhaps it would be better to talk to the king and agree with him about how to rule our land," she begged.

"I have tried to work with the conquering king," Gospatric said angrily. "I have paid him a great sum of money. But all the foreigners want is to take our wealth and dominate us. Is that right? Should we submit, or should we fight?"

There was a band of warriors around Gospatric. "Let's go and fight the foreign king," they roared.

Gospatric had a plan.

"Do you think we should join with the Danes?" I heard Gospatric say to his men. "The king of the Danes wants to rule England in the place of William. They are great fighters. We can fight the Norman invaders together."

They all agreed to do this. Gospatric sent messages to those fearsome fighters whose longboats look like dragons flying over the water. People called them Vikings.

With his sword flashing and the mane of his warhorse flying, Gospatric led the noblemen away from the castle by the sea at Bamburgh. They stormed southwards, across the River Wansbeck, across the Tyne, towards York where they had agreed to meet the Danes. I was among the servants and the horses who followed. We left behind the women and children in the castle as we all rode off to battle.

We camped in the forests, hiding from the enemy and waiting for the dragon boats to arrive. At last we saw two hundred and forty Danish boats coming, all of them full of ferocious fighting men. It was a most terrifying army. I had never seen anything like it. Surely with this army on our side, we would defeat the Normans.

I was watching from a distance as the two armies together turned to attack the city of York which was held by King William's men. In a horrific battle Gospatric and his men killed all the Norman soldiers and burned the city to the ground. Many women and children and helpless old people suffered cruel deaths when the city was burned. There was screaming and crying and a terrible noise everywhere.

After their victory, Gospatric and his men gathered around a campfire feasting and drinking. I and the other servants brought them food and wine. The men were talking about what to do next.

"We have surely destroyed King William's army," they said to each other. "Let's go home now, and leave the Danes here in York. King William knows now that he cannot defeat us. The Danes can be left in charge."

And so we went home. You can imagine how relieved Gospatric's wife and family were to see him safe again in their castle at Bamburgh. But this was not the end of the story. The Northumbrian lords had made one bad mistake.

They had left the Danes in York, and winter was coming. There was no food or shelter for them in the burned city. They began to get hungry and cold, and there was little shelter in their boats. If there is no food, an army can't survive. After a miserable winter, many of the Danes had suffered enough and sailed back where they had come from. This gave an opportunity to King William and his Normans.

They did a terrible thing which the people of the north of England have never forgotten.

I heard the story as I served the wine and the meat to my lord Gospatric and the family in the castle.

King William destroys Northumbria

King William had decided that he would never again allow the Northumbrian armies to rebel against him.

He spoke to his soldiers: "Your job now is to destroy the north. If there are no farms with food and animals the people cannot fight us. You are to drive everyone from the villages. Spare nobody. Kill the animals and burn the barns. Destroy the countryside."

The soldiers did as the king commanded. They started near York and they worked their way north.   All the people were driven away or killed; the mothers and their babies, the old grandfathers and grandmothers who had no way to fight, the children and the young men and women who ploughed the fields. Very few managed to escape. The soldiers burned the crops and the ploughs so that no new food could be grown the following year. They slaughtered the cows and the calves, the sheep and the lambs, and all the animals.

As the killings went on the soldiers were coming closer and closer to our castle at Bamburgh. We all lived in daily fear that the soldiers would burn everything and kill us too, but King William had different plans for Northumberland.

He marched with his army to Scotland. The Scottish king was not as powerful as the new foreign king and he was forced to agree that he would not send his armies to England.

Exile to Scotland

On his way back from Scotland King William did something dreadful to punish Gospatric.

"If I am to be ruler of all of England, Gospatric must go!" he thundered. "I cannot give him the chance to lead another rebellion. I will no longer allow him to be the earl of Northumberland, and I will put a Norman in his place. I shall send him away from Bamburgh for ever."

He sent messengers to our castle. My lord Gospatric was horrified. He had to leave, or the king might kill him and his family.

"We must leave our home," I heard him say to his lady wife. "Pack up all our things. We must sail away in our boats to Scotland."

"How can we bear to do this?" the lady wailed. "Where will we go? Who will take care of us?"

"We will seek shelter from my cousin Malcolm, the king of Scotland," replied Gospatric.

So the family escaped in boats and sailed north. I joined the men who drove their herds of cattle away, over the lands which had belonged to Gospatric's family for as long as anyone could remember. The Scottish king was very kind and gave a large part of his land to the family. They built a castle by the sea at a place called Dunbar.

Now I have a question for you. You will remember that I had heard his wife begging him not to go to war.

Do you think she was right? Would it have been better to decide with the conquering King William how the land should be ruled? Or do you think Gospatric should have fought against the Normans?

Rightly or wrongly, the Northumbrians were brave soldiers and would not bow down before the foreign king. They fought, but they lost the battle, and were driven away into Scotland. Now the family had to settle in another land, and I as a servant boy had to go with them.

There is now no strong leader to defend Northumberland. There is nothing to stop the Norman invaders.

Earl Robert marries Matilda

Matilda

Robert de Mowbray

1095

My name is Robert de Mowbray, and I am a Norman. I am the earl of Northumberland, the strongest and most important man in all this part of England. I live in my castle at Bamburgh. Everybody is afraid of me. I am going to tell you how I helped to defeat those foolish English people.

The boastful earl of Northumberland

I had taken part in the Battle of Hastings with my friend William de Merlay when we were only boys. My uncle the bishop of Coutances was a close friend of the new King William of England. I knew that I would become important and powerful, but I had to wait for my chance.

So I followed my uncle the bishop in all his wars around England. As you may know, bishops are not allowed to kill people themselves, and he found me very useful. I never minded killing my enemies. I was glad to do it. I didn't care if they screamed and cried as they bled to death.

People are afraid of me because now I am a large, strong man. If anyone looks at me the wrong way I am ready to fight.

After the rebellion by Gospatric and those ridiculous Northumbrians, King William destroyed the north. He needed a new man to keep order and to stop them rising again. Who would he choose?

My uncle spoke to the king. "My lord," he said. "Would you allow my nephew Robert de Mowbray to become the earl of Northumberland?"

The king asked Bishop Geoffrey what kind of man I was.

"My lord, he is courageous in battle and he is not afraid to kill his enemies," replied my uncle.

The king agreed, and now I am the earl of Northumberland. I am in charge of the king's castle at Newcastle and the one at Bamburgh which had once belonged to the family of Gospatric.

No-one gives me orders. I am so strong that I can do what I like. Even the king doesn't frighten me. But I have so much land to control that I needed some help. I went to my friend William de Merlay.

"William, I need a strong man in a place called Morpeth," I said to him. "I need a castle to guard an important river crossing there. The king of Scotland and his supporters may come that way to fight us."

William was very happy to agree. This is what he had been waiting for. It was his reward for faithfully following King William, Bishop Geoffrey and now me. He would have his own land to rule and become the lord of Morpeth. The first thing he needed to do was to build a castle by the Wansbeck river.

Building the castle at Morpeth
Together our soldiers forced the people of Morpeth to build William's castle. Our men shouted orders at them even though they couldn't understand our language. They are so stupid. They hated us, but I didn't care. I just laughed at them. We had plenty of weapons, and we made them obey us. Even the children had to work for us. We chose a hill by the river.

"Build the hill higher. Dig those ditches. Cut down those trees. Build the tower. Build the walls." We yelled orders at them until the work was done.

When the castle was built, William de Merlay felt strong and safe.

"I am ready to marry now and start a family," he told me. "I want sons who will be lords of Morpeth after me. I will always support you, Robert de Mowbray. I will help you become more and more powerful."

Around this time, King William died. His son William Rufus became the new king of England, but he lived far away in the south, and I wasn't going to let him order me around. I was the ruler of Northumberland, and I had a strong supporter in Morpeth.

Robert de Mowbray kills a king
I told you I am a man who doesn't care who he kills if it will help me become more powerful. I did something that not many people would dare

to do. I let my men kill the king of Scotland. Why shouldn't I?

I found out that King Malcolm had crossed the border from Scotland into Northumberland.

"Try to capture the king of Scotland," I told my men. "If you get the chance, don't be afraid to kill him."

My soldiers ambushed the Scottish king near Alnwick. During the fighting that followed, they killed both him and his son Edward.

People told me that his wife Queen Margaret was so sad that she died shortly after hearing the news but that was nothing to me. People disliked me for what I had done. They said I should have held him captive and demanded a huge ransom, but I didn't care. I had got rid of someone who wanted to take my lands.

The earl takes a wife

Things have become better and better for me. Not long ago, a messenger came to my castle.

"Your uncle Bishop Geoffrey has died in Normandy," the man told me. "He has left all his lands and treasure to you. My lord, now you are one of the most important men in all of England."

And he bowed low before me.

I decided that like William de Merlay, I would take a wife. I wanted a girl from a rich family who would make me more powerful than ever. I would marry her and take her to my castle. And so I married a young girl called Matilda.

Don't you agree that that was a clever thing for me to do?

Now we are living in Bamburgh, where no-one can injure me. We are safe behind the strong walls of our castle. I don't care if she likes me or not. I am her master.

My name is Matilda. I am going to tell you what happened to my husband, the wicked Earl Robert.

No choice but to marry the hairy earl

Around the time when Earl Robert had just killed the king of Scotland, my father, Richard de Laigle, told me that I was to marry him. I was just a girl of about fifteen. Can you imagine how I felt when I saw this man, all dark and hairy, who had an angry look on his face all the time?

I didn't want to marry him but I had no choice. My father told me that he was one of the richest men in the land, and that I should be happy to be his bride. Nothing I said made any difference. Robert de Mowbray carried me away to his castle at Bamburgh.

I didn't like being married to him one bit. He tormented me spitefully. He was a hateful bully. But it was not long before he came to a dreadful end and it was his own fault.

He was out riding near the sea with his men when he saw some longboats coming from Norway.

"Let us take these boats. They are full of valuable merchandise," he said to his men. He was afraid of no-one. They captured the boats and stole the goods.

The Norwegian merchants complained to King William Rufus.

"You must come to my court here in the south of England," the king ordered my husband. "You must explain your crime."

But my husband refused to go. He obeyed no-one, and he was not afraid of the king.

King William Rufus was very angry.

"We will put an end to this rebellious earl in Northumberland for once and always," he said. He assembled his knights in armour on their horses and all their men.

They rode north to Newcastle and took my husband's castle there. Then the king's army marched towards Morpeth to the castle of his supporter, William de Merlay.

He and many of his knights were feasting when the king's soldiers suddenly attacked. They captured the castle. William's wife managed to escape in the darkness with the help of the servants, her baby in her arms and the children by her side. William and many of the knights were taken away as prisoners.

Then the king's army marched to the castle at Bamburgh where I lived with my husband. The army surrounded us. I was terrified.

"Come out of there. Open the gates," ordered the king's men. But my husband refused.

Then we watched as the army built a tall wooden tower. From that height, they could attack us in the castle, and also they could wait until we ran out of food and were forced to open the gates.

One night however my husband escaped over the walls of the castle. Unfortunately for him he was captured by the king's soldiers.

The king will put out his eyes
After my husband was taken prisoner, I was left in charge of the castle. But the king had a cruel plan. He ordered his soldiers to stand my husband where I could see him as I looked over the walls.

"Open the gates, Lady Matilda!" the king ordered me. "You see this spike? Open the gates, or my soldier will push it into your husband's eyes, one after the other, and he will be blinded."

What could I do? I didn't love my husband, but I had no choice. How could I allow him to be blinded before my very eyes?

"Open the gates," I said to our soldiers. "We must surrender the castle."

What is your opinion? Do you think I did right to stop the king from blinding my husband?

Right or not, that was the end of Robert de Mowbray's good luck. The king's soldiers put him in chains and took him to a prison in Windsor castle which is far away in the south of England. He will stay there for the rest of his life.

I am really glad that I will never see him again.

> My name is Juliana. I am the granddaughter of Gospatric who was sent away from Northumberland to Scotland by King William the Conqueror. I am going to tell you how I came to Morpeth.

The castle by the sea

I loved my home in Scotland where I lived with my family in our castle by the sea. I would play on the beach with my brothers, climb on the cliffs and jump over the waves.

My parents always told my brothers and me stories about those days long ago when the king drove our family away. We longed to take Northumberland back from the conquerors.

One day, a group of important people came to our castle at Dunbar. I was only a little girl at the time. I watched the horsemen, messengers who had been sent from the king of England. My brothers and I were peeping round the doors because we weren't allowed to go near the strangers.

"Welcome to my castle," I heard my father say to the chief of the visitors who was dressed in rich armour and clothing. "My men will see to your horses. Come in and rest."

The newcomers were speaking in a language which we did not understand. Our father's men took the strangers' horses and brushed them down, giving them food and water

"Why are these people here?" I asked my mother Sibilla.

"They are going to write an agreement," she replied. "The new king of England, King Henry, has agreed to give your father back some of the lands your grandfather lost in Northumberland."

My father gave the visitors a delicious meal. My older brother Edgar was allowed to help serve the visitors. There was wine and roasted meat.

The feast went on through the night while the waves were crashing against the cliffs below the castle walls, and we children went to sleep. The next day, the strangers sat around the table with our father and his important friends. There were many discussions, and at times some loud voices. Then our mother Sibilla and the servants would pour some wine and things would calm down.

In the end, they came to an agreement. One of the strangers read out the words on a little piece of sheepskin called a charter. It was not in English, nor was it in the French language that these strangers were speaking. My mother told us that it was in Latin, which is the language of writing.

One of the men told us in our language what the writing said. King Henry had given our father the right to hold some lands in Northumberland, in the borders between England and Scotland.

In return for these lands, he had to take charge of all the people moving through them. The ingoing and outgoing, it was called. He was to prevent the enemies of King Henry coming down from Scotland to attack England.

"Now it is time to sign this agreement," said one of the strangers.

Our father didn't know how to write. He made a cross, one line over the other, on the charter. The stranger wrote our father's name, Count Gospatric. Next, some of the important men made their crosses and the stranger wrote their names.

Soon after that the visitors went away. Our father was becoming an important man in Northumberland.

This is what he told us. "I now have the right to ride on horseback over the hills and fields in Northumberland, with our dogs, hunting the deer and other wild animals. Everyone who lives in these places will see me, and know that I am their lord, and that they must obey me."

The girl must marry the foreigner
That was not the end of the story. There were always people coming and going at our family castle. They would bring their horses and their

soldiers. The women and servants would cook great banquets while we children played around. In the evenings they would sit around the fire and people would tell stories about their ancestors and the battles they had fought long ago.

I was fourteen years old, and growing up to be a beautiful young woman. I was no longer a wild girl, running around on the sands beside the sea. My mother would comb my long fair hair and plait it down behind my back. She made me a beautiful red dress and when I wore it I thought I looked as lovely as a princess. I still wanted to ride my pony and play in the sea, but I knew that the times were changing for me. I would soon be grown up

"Juliana, my dear," my mother Sibilla said to me one day. "Before long, you will have to leave this place. Your father and I are looking for a husband for you. You will go away and be the mistress of a castle of your own."

"But Mother, I don't want to leave," I said. "I don't want to go far away and never see you again."

"I know, Juliana," she replied. "But you are the daughter of a great family, and you must marry and have children. If we can find you a good husband, you will have servants and guards to protect you."

So I would dream about a handsome young lord who would one day come and take me away to his castle. Sometimes that made me happy but at other times I was very afraid. There were so many wars and battles, and the men were always telling stories of people who were killed and wounded.

One day, my father and my brother Edgar, who by this time was a grown man, left our castle with a group of men. They sailed away into England. They were gone for quite a long time, a couple of weeks or more. When they came back, they had a charter in a roll, which they showed to my mother and me. They had been to Northumberland, and the arrangements were made.

My father took me aside.

"My dear daughter Juliana," he said. "I have arranged with King Henry of England that you will marry a man called Ranulph. He is the son of a man called William de Merlay who came to England with the great King William the Conqueror. The family has a castle in a place called Morpeth."

"Why must I marry this man?" I asked my father. I didn't want to marry into the family who had been among my grandfather's enemies.

"This is very important for our family," he replied. "The new King Henry wants peace between Scotland and England. He has given us land in Northumberland. You will help to bring peace between the two countries."

"But Father, how can I go away from you and my mother?" I said. "What if I don't love him? Is he handsome? Is he kind? How shall I understand him if he speaks that French language?"

"You are a lucky girl," my father insisted. "You will soon be the mistress of your own castle. God willing, you will become a mother of sons, and a clever girl like you will soon learn that language."

So it was arranged that I, Juliana, a daughter of the great Gospatric family, was to marry Ranulph de Merlay of Morpeth. I was part of King Henry's plan.

Juliana comes to Morpeth
Once I knew what was going to happen to me, I cried into my pillow every night.

For the next few weeks, the household was busy getting everything ready for me to leave. The servants were packing clothes and linens for me into chests. My brothers watched all the preparations. My eldest brother Edgar wasn't always kind.

"This castle will be quieter without you, Juliana," he would say. "Now we'll all have some peace from your squealing and running around." And he would make me cry, tickling me and pinching me.

On the day I left, the horsemen came to take me down to the boat.

"Goodbye, my dearest daughter," my mother Sibilla said. We were both trying to hide our tears.

We hugged each other tightly, and then I had to leave. I have never seen her since that day. I looked back at my castle on the cliff, but then I turned around towards the new place where I would live with my husband.

I would like to ask you this question. Do you think that my father and the king were right to decide together that I should marry the young lord Ranulph de Merlay?

But I had no choice. I came from Scotland to this castle beside the river in Morpeth. I am learning my husband's French language, and even sometimes he tries to speak in English to me. My husband is a soldier, but my job is to become a mother of baby boys. That is what I must do. I wonder if I will succeed.

Juliana says farewell to her mother

1113

Sibilla
Juliana

Village girl washes the pots in the Wansbeck river

1120

Ebba

32

My name is Ebba. I am a servant in the castle at Morpeth, and my mistress is called Juliana. My job is to do all the nasty dirty work at the castle. I cannot tell you how old I am, but it is something like the number you can see if I hold up all my fingers. I am going to tell you about my life.

The life of a poor girl

I was born in a hut beside the river Wansbeck. It is dark and muddy inside. I am the oldest child, and my little brothers and sisters are always crawling around in the dirt. My mother and father go out early in the morning and take the oxen to the fields. They work very hard to grow food, and often they are forced to give food to the people in the castle so that we don't have enough to eat ourselves.

My work was to stay at home watching the little ones and I would give them the pieces of bread that my mother had left for them. But often they ran away, and I didn't know where they were. They came back even hungrier and dirtier. That is how I lived.

Ebba must work at the castle

I was growing older, and one day a man from the castle came to our hut. I watched him from the shadows. He spoke our language and he stared at me.

"The family in the castle need a servant," he said. My mother looked down at the ground. She was afraid of the man.

When my father came in later, he spoke to me.

"You will have to do what the man wants," he said. "This family belongs to the lord in the castle, and whatever they say, we have to do it."

So I had to obey. I do all the dirty jobs. I empty the smelly chamber pots every morning and feed the pigs. I have to kill the chickens and pluck out their feathers and prepare them for eating. The other servants are often unkind to me. They slap me and tell me to hurry up with my jobs.

One good thing is that sometimes I can hide away bones or crusts of bread which are left on the dinner table. It doesn't matter if people have already chewed on them. I am supposed to give them to the dogs and the pigs but I put them in my pocket for my little brothers and sisters when no-one is looking. The children are so hungry they suck the bones and gobble up the crusts.

I don't like being in the castle. I only understand a little of the language that the family speak. Sometimes the lord looks at me in a nasty way. He tries to touch me. Then I run away but I am always afraid that one day he will hurt me.

The lady Juliana is kinder. She speaks my language, but she has three boys who are rude and unkind. They pinch me and pull my hair. They say things that I don't understand, and they laugh. No-one stops them.

I like to come down to the river and clean the pots because I am away from the castle. I pick up handfuls of grass with the river sand in the roots and rub the pots until all traces of food are cleaned away. It is a pleasant job in the cool river water. I can see the oxen and my mother and father working on the long ridges of earth.

I wonder what will happen to me? Will I be cleaning the pots and feeding the pigs for the people in the castle all of my life? Or might I live with a man in a hut and have children like my mother?

Sometimes I dream that a rich young lord will marry me and take me away to his castle where I will live like Lady Juliana. But I know really that this is just a dream. My life will be like my mother's, nothing but work and hunger and sickness. There will be no happy ending for me. I will always be a servant girl.

What do you think? It is right that a girl like me may not choose her own life?

My name is Eustorcia, and I am the daughter of William de Merlay, the lord of Morpeth. I am going to tell you about the last days of my father's life.

William de Merlay is afraid of the devils

My father came from Normandy many years ago when he was just a boy. He had followed his master the bishop in many battles. But he knew that when he died, his soul would go to purgatory, and there he would suffer until all his bad deeds were cleaned away. He did wicked things, wounding and even killing other people. Perhaps the devil would take him down to hell and torture him for ever.

When he was ill, and afraid of dying, he would picture those awful devils coming to take him away.

So he made a plan. If he made a gift to the church, the monks and priests would pray for him and his family, and that would help to save him from the tortures of hell.

"I have decided to give the monks of the holy church of St Cuthbert at Durham some of my lands", he said to my mother. "I will give them a place called Morwick near the River Coquet, and as well I will give them one of my fisheries on the River Tyne."

My mother thought that was a good idea. There was a great day of celebration in our castle when the agreement was made. My brothers Ranulph, Goffrid and Morel were old enough to take part. The monks had ridden on their horses, and our men put them in the stables and brushed them down. Everyone was assembled in the great hall.

The monks took out the charter with all the writing on. They got their pens of long goose feathers ready.

"William de Merlay, you have made a great gift to our holy church," one of them said. "We will reward you by praying for your soul and for your wife and all your children."

He read out the words on the charter in the Latin language, but none of us understood that. My father William signed the charter with a cross. After that, my brothers Ranulph, Goffrid and Morel and some other men did the same.

No-one expected me to make the cross because I am a girl. My mother neither. But we knew the monks would pray for us too, and that made us feel very happy.

Once the signing was completed, all the men sat down together and had a great feast. My mother served the visitors with our best wine.

Everyone was pleased. My father had done a very good thing by helping to save our eternal souls.

The monks were happy because they needed the lands to grow food, and the fish for their meals when they are not allowed to eat meat.

Will the family rule Morpeth for ever?
I know that my father will die very soon, and we will all be sad. But the time must come to him as to everyone. He has had such a long life, coming all the way from Le Merlerault in Normandy, helping to conquer England, and building his castle here in Morpeth.

When that day comes, my brother Ranulph will become the new lord of Morpeth with his wife Juliana at his side. Their son William, will become the next lord, in his turn, when Ranulph dies. We are the conquerors. I think the de Merlay family will rule Morpeth for ever.

Do you think so too?

Dear older readers and adults

The stories in this short book have been abstracted from my carefully researched book, *Juliana and Ranulph of Morpeth Castle*. I've selected tales which I think are of special interest to young people and raised some of the challenges they show.

I have had to craft the stories into simpler shapes than might have existed in reality, without losing the essence of the facts and the truth. It has been hard to think of the right words which describes this process: to formulate them; to simplify them; to mould them; to craft them?

An example of this is the battle at York. There were many more characters involved than Gospatric on the Northumbrian side, and various phases to the battles. It was some time later before Gospatric and his family were exiled to Scotland. These events were recorded by the monk chroniclers Simeon of Durham and Orderic Vitalis.

Also, we do not know for certain that William de Merlay and Robert de Mowbray were actually at the invasion of 1066. Robert's father was in the hall at the call to arms, as was Bishop Geoffrey, and it is likely that William's father was too. The young men may have been there. Certainly Bishop Geoffrey of Coutances was their master, and they were in his service at or soon after this time. I have formulated/moulded/crafted the two boys into telling their stories as though they were there. The scene in the hall of Normandy was described by Orderic Vitalis. The one before the battle of Hastings is based on writings by the Norman poet Wace.

If you would like to know the more complex realities, do please read *Juliana and Ranulph of Morpeth Castle*, where the facts as they exist are fully referenced. Even in the adults' book, there are many uncertainties, especially as there are only a few hard facts from this almost forgotten time in Morpeth's history. In such a full account, one can reflect on the problems, and have many phrases such as "it could be", "it is likely", "it is possible", or "on the other hand". This vagueness is not, I suggest, suitable for children. There is plenty of time as they grow older to deal with these uncertainties.

Another difficulty was how to make the chronological leaps between the stories, and how to help the readers remember the way in which the characters related to one another. I'm not sure if this has been totally successful. After quite a lot of re-thinking, and comments from my readers, I have written each story from a particular point in the characters' lives. We hear how they came to arrive at that position, but we do not necessarily find out what happens to them later. To find that out, for example what happens to Lady Matilda after her husband was imprisoned, you can go to *Juliana and Ranulph of Morpeth Castle*.

Special thanks must go to my adult readers, Alice Butler, Laura Gubbins, Dinah Iredale and Karen Tweddle, for their helpful comments.

Even more so, perhaps, thanks should go to my young listeners, my grandsons Ralph Ashton age 11, Guy Gubbins age 9 and Al Gubbins age 7. Questions they raised as I read the stories to them at bedtime have all been dealt with. They certainly always wanted to know the ages of the children who told the stories, and if it hadn't been for them, I would never have thought that perhaps Ebba, a girl who had had no education, might not have known her age.

Bridget Gubbins
Morpeth, 2017